RUBIES &
SAPPHIRES

Text and Photographs
Fred Ward

Editing
Charlotte Ward

The **Panther Brooch,** *made for the Duchess of Windsor, features a 152-carat Sri Lanka blue sapphire.*

Cartier's

These three glorious stars reside at Washington's Smithsonian Institution.
Star of Asia *(top) 330 cts.*
Star of Bombay *(right) 182 cts.*
Rosser Reeves Ruby *(bottom) 138 cts.*

1

HISTORY
AND LORE

Rubies—the color of passion and love's own hue, gems that glow red as no others. Whatever primeval chord they strike deep within us rings almost universally. Their charisma seduces a world of willing subjects. Potentates, emperors, and maharajahs have risked all to possess their beauty. And the beautiful have risked all to call rubies their own.

Many people express great surprise to learn that rubies have a fraternal twin, one with little visible family resemblance and a separate illustrious romantic history. Rubies' natural sisters are sapphires. As different as they look, rubies and sapphires are composed of the same material, aluminum oxide (corundum), a relatively common mineral in the earth's crust. But as fine transparent gem crystals, corundum is rare.

All corundum gem crystals except one—every color of the rainbow—are sapphires. When gem corundum is red, it alone is ruby. In a pure state, corundum, and thus sapphire, is colorless. Tiny trace amounts of other materials determine the fabulous hues that make rubies and sapphires the treasures we love. A minute amount of chromium makes rubies red. The blue in sapphires comes from the simultaneous presence of titanium and iron. Iron causes yellow. Various other elements and concentrations color sapphires pink, lavender, orange, green, purple, and peach-apricot.

Remarkably, until the mastery of chemistry in the 1700s much of the world did not even recognize rubies and sapphires as family members. Once people knew that rubies and sapphires were different colors of the same material and that sapphires came in every color, then they realized that corundum accounts for half of the four major gemstones alongside diamonds and emeralds. In some places rubies and sapphires occur together, as in Burma (Myanmar) and Sri Lanka (formerly Ceylon), where they are found in the same mines or a few miles apart. Madagascar, Kenya, Thailand, and Tanzania have both gems, but in separate locations. Montana, China, Australia, and several African countries produce only sapphires.

From the legendary ruby and sapphire mines at Mogok, Burma, the 196-carat **Hixon Ruby** *is one of the finest gem crystals ever found.*

Hixon Ruby from Natural History Museum of Los Angeles County
Starfish bracelet by Mayfield's Inc.

Government of Myanmar

For most people in the West the first references to rubies they hear are from the Bible. All relate to the value of the stones; two compare rubies to wisdom and two compare them to women. Three of the references appear in Proverbs:

> *She is more precious than rubies.*
> *For wisdom is above rubies.*
> *Who can find a virtuous woman? For her price is above rubies.*

The fourth is in Job:

> *For the price of wisdom is above rubies.*

Jews believe rubies are the most precious of the 12 gems God created when making all things. Revered as the sacred gem of the tribe of Judah, ruby is the fourth stone set in Aaron's breastplate.

Most red Biblical jewels probably were not rubies. Before scientists classified gems and minerals by their atomic structure, the Greek scholar Theophrastus practiced a far more obvious system. Writing one of the earliest gem books about 315 B.C., he grouped stones by color. He categorized rubies, garnets, spinels, and other red gems as *carbuncles*, a name that referred to the color of glowing embers. Cutters knew there were differences because rubies and sapphires, so difficult to work with primitive tools and grit, took much longer to shape.

Large gem-quality rubies are among the rarest crystals on earth. A faceted gem ruby over 50 carats is almost unknown. Recently this remarkable 500-carat specimen (left), found in Burma, was named **The Mogok** *to honor the legendary gem center.*

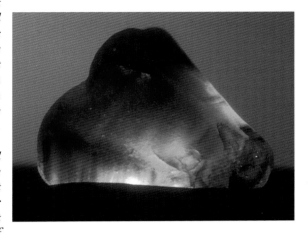

This great fist-sized crystal (right) from Sri Lanka may have been the world's finest uncut sapphire. Priced over $1 million, the 3965-carat treasure yielded a number of gems up to 100 carats.

Pliny might be called the world's first gemologist. In first-century Rome, he already knew a number of details that gemologists had to relearn in the last century. For instance, he noted that dealers deliberately simulated rubies in order to fool buyers, that a ruby's weight (specific gravity) was an identifier that separated it from other red stones, and that even with an unaided eye rubies could be verified by their natural inclusions (which the public often calls "flaws"). Before his death in A.D. 79, Pliny wrote on every known topic. In his magnum opus, *Natural History*, he noted that "carbunculi are imitated by glass and such imitations at first sight are excellent. False carbunculi are detected by lack of hardness of their powder and by their weight...further, one sees in false carbunculi certain small inclusions, that is blisters and vesicles, which look like silver."

While 10th-century European rulers stuffed their coffers with red spinels labeled "balas-rubies," Arab scientist Al-Biruni listed nearly exact specific gravities for spinels, rubies, and sapphires and separated them by name—*balkhash* for red spinel and *yaqut* for corundum. It would take another 700 to 800 years for scientists to confirm chemical differences.

Sapphires did not escape historical confusion. Just as the word *ruby* derives from the Latin *ruber* for red, our word *sapphire* is from the Latin form of the Greek word for blue. Similar Hebrew and Persian words also associate blue with sapphires. However, as with rubies, blue gemstones were first categorized by color, not chemistry. Both buyer and seller of any attractive blue gem probably called it sapphire. The most likely candidate for blue "sapphire" in the Old Testament is lapis lazuli from Afghanistan.

*Sri Lanka once was named Serendip. Surely finding such incredible
treasures on "Gem Island" parallels the tales of happy, unexpected
discoveries that gave us the word* serendipity.

With a profusion of colors, Sri Lanka, famed for magnificent blue sapphires, also has huge pinks, resplendent yellows, and most expensive of all sapphire colors, the luminous pinkish orange padparadschas.

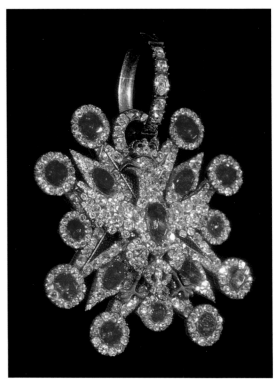

The Green Vaults, Dresden (2)

Researchers generally believe rubies and sapphires reached the Mediterranean area and Europe after the Old Testament during Greco-Roman times. India has the greatest love for and longest history with colored stones. Ancient records describe the "Gem Island" of Serendip, near India, where jewels washed down from the central mountains with every heavy rain. Such serendipity continues to this day on Sri Lanka, as Serendip is now called. One gem dealer recently joked, "We must be the most pious people on earth because we always walk with our heads bowed," referring to the local habit of continually looking for gemstones in fields and along the roads.

With their unprecedented history in rubies and sapphires, Asians have mined the largest stones and told the grandest tales. An old Hindu belief held that the god Krishna rewards supplicants who offer rubies; a good ruby assures rebirth as an emperor, lesser stones make only a king. A relatively common bit of folklore still repeated by peasants says all rubies start colorless and ripen with age. Sometimes this tale broadens to say that pink sapphires should be replanted until they become rubies and that gems with many inclusions are overripe.

The most famous early Western traveler through Asia, Marco Polo, wrote that the king of Serendip had a ruby over four inches long and as big as his finger. Such tales whetted the appetite of Europeans for exotic gems. And no wonder. The Asian penchant for ascribing magical powers to gems spread to the Continent, where rubies were said to cure circulation disorders

Throughout history royalty reserved precious stones for themselves. In the 1700s Europe's wealthy duke, August the Strong, of Saxony, assembled a fabulous gem collection, now in Dresden's Green Vaults (left).

Early Romans and Greeks learned to carve sapphires with images such as the woman with eagle (right).

India's Mogul rulers wore jade archery thumb rings decorated with rubies (below).

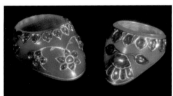

The British Museum, London

Fitzwilliam Museum at Cambridge University

and melancholia. Wearers of the red beauties could expect wisdom, health, happiness, and good luck in gambling and with the opposite sex. Who could resist that combination?

Once rubies and sapphires arrived in Europe, lore associated with colored gemstones took a turn to the dark side. Perhaps a colder climate put a chill on the hot tropical gems. Or maybe it was mixing jewels with Western religions. Whatever the reason, in medieval Europe some owners believed that rubies possessed magical powers to turn dull and dark as warnings to their owners. Legend has it that the downfall of Catherine of Aragon, first wife of Henry VIII, was presaged by the darkening of her ruby. A similar tale grimly reveals that Elizabeth, wife of Franz Joseph of Austria, always wore a ruby as a talisman—with the exception of one particular morning. Apparently she forgot to put it on—and was assassinated.

Most ruby lore extols the good luck and fortune the stone brings owners. It is no surprise that anyone would relate possession of such a rare and magnificent jewel with happiness and success. U Thein Lwin, the Myanmar Gems Enterprise advisor, says his countrymen call rubies *Ma Naw Ma Ya*, "Desire-Fulfilling Stones," because they make dreams come true. Burmese often consider rubies the "king of gems" and call all other stones including sapphires "attendants." Well-known international sapphire dealer Roland Naftule takes a different view, saying, "Rubies are gorgeous gems and certainly deserve their reputation, but there is nothing as beautiful as a richly colored sapphire."

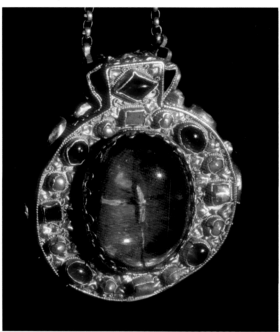

Some famous artifacts may not be what they seem. In the authentic 10th-century **Talisman of Charlemagne** *(left), glass and quartz stones, widely publicized as sapphires, sandwich what are said to be splinters of the True Cross.*

Yogo Gulch, Montana, discovered in 1879, was identified by Frederick Kunz as America's first sapphire mine. Needing no heat to be "cornflower blue," Yogos fetch the country's highest sapphire prices. These cufflink images of the owner's daughter (right) were carved in Amsterdam in 1902.

Cathedral Treasury, Reims

"I love them both," says Jack S.D. Abraham, a New York dealer in fine gems. "There are very solid reasons for owning both rubies and sapphires. But rubies have a special place in my heart. Among many people in the world with high and medium incomes, gems are the traditional means of transferring savings without paying oppressive taxes. Gems are a timeless hard currency. They are also durable. Crystals that sparkled 2000 years ago will continue to sparkle long after whole civilizations turn to dust."

In fact, the intertwining stories of people and gemstones weaves one of the oldest threads through time. Every culture that has come into contact with gem crystals has loved and coveted them. Whether the prevailing allure relates to magic, power, wealth, beauty, durability, or rarity, the historical reality remains. Early humans formed an integral bond with gemstones that remains unbroken. Geology, gemology, and chemistry now tell us the molecular structure of gems, their age, where they come from, and how we can duplicate the process of creating them. But the ultimate appeal defies description. We know innately that gems possess a fundamental beauty and that they are valuable beyond almost every other object on earth. As a European collector once told me, "Spend $50,000 on your wife or girlfriend for a fur coat or a car. In 10 years she has a rag or a wreck. Use the same money to buy her a fine gem, and she has a treasure worth even more over time, which she can pass along to her children."

Gems are concentrated, portable wealth. What was true historically remains relevant today. As relatively comfortable Westerners we may forget the cyclical nature of the rise and fall of countries, institutions, and personal wealth. During periods of turmoil, paper may become worthless. Money,

stocks, bonds, and homes often lose their value. Markets fluctuate, and governments never last forever. People who live in troubled times and places know to put something aside in case of crisis. Most often they collect gems because of their almost universal acceptance and unprecedented price-to-weight concentration. Think about transporting a million dollars. That million in dollar bills, almost a ton of money, would occupy 42 cubic feet of space. A million-dollar gold brick (with $400-an-ounce gold) would be difficult to lift at 156 pounds. But the 88-carat padparadscha sapphire on page 43, which recently sold for several million dollars, weighed just over half an ounce (about the weight of a quarter and a half dollar). Several beautiful natural rubies have sold for more than $225,000 a carat. The red diamond in the Smithsonian Institution cost more than a million dollars for less than a carat!

People ask me continually if there are any differences between "old" and "new" gems. Every gemstone that has been mined or will be mined in our lifetime is already millions of years old. For a gem to be so near the surface that people can uncover it means it has been pushed to or through the earth's crust by the effects of mountain building, upthrusting of the land, or volcanic explosions. It is intriguing to think that new gemstones are forming this very minute, miles beneath our feet. However, it may take tens to hundreds of millions of years until they surface for our planet's future inhabitants. Thus, there is no real difference between old and new gems as far as quality, value, durability, and beauty are concerned. The only difference is whether the gems have already been mined or are still underground waiting to be discovered and mined.

THE HUNT FOR
TREASURE

I nternational dealers joke that gems seem to occur in the worst, most remote areas of Third World countries. Many do, but there are some remarkable and surprising exceptions. Rubies and sapphires have a long history in Asia. Although we do not know a precise date and place, most likely natives of India and Sri Lanka first appreciated rubies and sapphires 2000 to 5000 years ago. Even corundum, the mineral name for rubies and sapphires, probably came from the Hindi word *kauruntaka*. For millennia the great gemstones that now fill royal vaults and public museums were mainly bought and sold in India.

Because of their beauty, color, and hardness, crystals fascinated and mystified early humans. Over the centuries Sri Lanka consistently produced stunning varieties of pink, blue, and yellow sapphires, in addition to red, pink, and blue star corundum. Scholars have dated Middle Eastern jewelry studded with gems as early as 3000 B.C. Even then, India was well known for large quantities of medium quality, moderate-sized rubies and for enhancing other gemstones. King Tut's Egyptian tomb, dug for the boy king about 1300 B.C., contained red agate and carnelian, which had been treated and assembled in India 700 years earlier.

India's importance in the gem trade developed over generations of relative political stability with dozens of maharajahs and thousands of court members as potential buyers. Potentates, ruling a subcontinent blessed with a wide variety of gemstones, coveted jewels and gathered craftsmen who learned to fashion them. A huge domestic and foreign market burgeoned into the world gem-trading center for diamonds, rubies, sapphires, pearls, lapis lazuli, agate, and garnets.

Today India no longer produces such significant quantities of diamonds and pearls. It does maintain a thriving business in small, relatively inexpensive rubies, the translucent to opaque red or purple crystals that most

Because together rubies and sapphires occur in all colors of the spectrum, it is only logical that designers create jewelry to celebrate this rainbow connection. Judy Mayfield specializes in multicolor bracelets.

Rainbow sapphire bracelets and
starfish pin from Mayfield's Inc.

13

Dug by hand, Kenya's Aqua Mine, north of the Tanzanian border, has produced a steady supply of rubies for years. Most of the output goes to Thailand for marketing.

In an attempt to control animal poaching, the Kenya government closed the area to everyone including miners for two years. Ruby theft is now a larger threat.

often decorate lower-priced necklaces and earrings. In addition to mining several different usually inexpensive gemstones today, India is a major world cutting center. Specializing in faceting smaller, less costly gems, Indians cut and polish diamonds, emeralds, rubies, cubic zirconia, and other stones in an industry worth hundreds of millions of dollars a year.

Sri Lanka is a wonderland for gem and crystal enthusiasts. Properly nicknamed the "Gem Island," its southern two-thirds is awash with jewels. A central mountain range holds the original treasure that millions of years of rains and erosion have generously spread throughout the island. Traditional mines are unheard of. As gem dealer Tom Ellawala and I walked through Paradise Estate, a large plain already mined five times, he explained, "Mechanization is prohibited here as a safety valve. At current mining rates our supplies will last for decades. This way we stretch our resources while employing as many people as possible."

All farmers are potential miners, routinely plowing up gems. Because most gem sites are alluvial, landowners lease low-lying rice paddies for repeated digging. Heavier than rocks and other gems, rubies and sapphires tend to accumulate at the bottom of gravel layers. So, when miners hit gravel, they almost always find gems. The largest sapphire crystal I ever saw,

Sri Lanka, formerly named Ceylon, abounds in gems. Any citizen may mine with an easy-to-obtain permit, and at some time during their lives most people do. Although individuals and small groups organized by investors have worked Paradise Estates (left) at least five times, it still yields enough sapphires to turn a profit for new leaseholders.

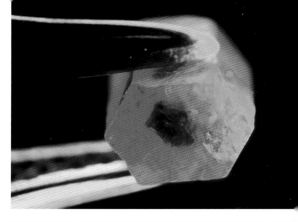

With the 1992 discovery at Mong Hsu, Burma produced enough rubies to lower market prices. Mong Hsu is less important today. Although typically small, Mong Hsu rubies often exhibit blue cores (upper right), which can be removed by heating. Burma and other Third World countries frustrate the gem trade with inferior faceting because they use primitive cutting equipment (right) and unskilled labor on some of the world's great gemstones.

© Tony Laughter, RW Hughes Collection (2)

weighing more than 10 kilograms, was uncovered in 1990 by a homeowner excavating a new basement.

The magic word for rubies and sapphires is Burma. Nothing like Burma's appeal exists for any other gem source except possibly for Colombia with its emeralds. No woman brags, "Oh, look at my Siberian diamond," or suggests that her engagement ring is better because it came from Namibia. In fact, it is unlikely that she or her jeweler knows or could find out the origin of her diamond. But the same buyer might lean across the counter to stipulate, "I want a pigeon-blood ruby from Burma." Fine rubies are typically sold as being either from Burma or not from Burma. And many an owner extends a hand and proudly asserts, "It's from Burma."

At the epicenter of the world market in two important areas, color and price, Burma rubies hold an unprecedented allure for buyers, despite (or perhaps because of) limited production and a huge reliance on smuggling in order for gems to reach the outside world. The world trade reveres "Burma red," or "pigeon blood" as an almost mystical standard. And this special appeal determines price. When two rubies of comparable quality are offered for sale, the one from Burma often fetches twice as much. Buyers should ask where a ruby under consideration originated.

M ogok, regarded by gem traders and historians alike as the mineral Mecca, has been an almost inaccessible wonderland filled with treasures and secrets. The ruby and sapphire mining region in Upper Burma was off-limits to foreigners for three decades after a military government took control in 1962. That government's descendant, still a military regime, renamed the country Myanmar and loosened travel restrictions. Although maps reflect the new name, no one in the gem trade calls the country's most famous products "Myanmar Rubies."

In 1991 I was the first journalist allowed to visit Mogok in the almost 30 years since 1962. In Rangoon at the annual Gems, Jade, and Pearl Emporium I watched $1.3 million of gems (along with more than $10 million of jade and pearls) auctioned to invited international dealers. Then I flew to Mandalay for a

"Big Mama," one of the largest Burma ruby crystals ever found, tips the scale at 10,100 carats. Such treasures are great mineral specimens and collector's items but are not sufficiently crystallized to be used as fine gems.

six-hour pot-hole-pounding drive north under the watchful eyes of two armed soldiers.

For more than 800 years the Mogok Stone Tract, as the British called it, has produced what most dealers and the buying public accept as the world's finest rubies and sapphires. Nestled in a mountainous bowl 4,000 feet high, Mogok is the only city of consequence in a mining area that extends about 20 by 20 miles. Europeans arriving in Burma in the 15th century described a thriving local trade in rubies. The first European to reach Mogok was probably Portuguese priest Pere Guiseppe d'Amato in 1833. His description of "square-set" mining, where workers dig a square hole vertically to a gravel layer, precisely matched the procedures I observed still being used. The adventurous father reported that Chinese merchants traversed the mountains annually to barter nutmeg, cloves, carpets, and cloth for gems.

Times changed for Mogok and Burma in 1885 when England annexed the area as part of its India holdings. The Burma kings, who had ruled from Mandalay, had maintained a rigid policy of possessing all gems above a certain size and quality. Noncompliance could have meant being burned alive. A major British target during their takeover, along with the king, was the royal gem collection, which the army expected to snare when it captured

Long hidden from view, the world's most famous ruby and sapphire mines surround Mogok in upper Burma. Once the perquisite of kings, later chartered to a British mining company, the area is now mined by the socialist government of Myanmar (Burma) and locals.

The relatively new central wash plant in Mogok handles several of the local ruby and sapphire mines. High-pressure hoses blast away the dirt, leaving gravel and gems to pass over vibrating screens. Heavier, the gems drop to the bottom, making them easier to retrieve once the worker flips the screen upside down.

Mining rubies and sapphires in most of the world is a labor-intensive, low-tech task. In one of Vietnam's new ruby mining areas near Quy Chau (left), workers pick into a hill, dropping dirt and gravel into buckets for washing. Vietnam's first rubies were confused with Burma's, and its fine electric-bright pink sapphires stunned the market. Supplies seem unreliable, and once again Burma's output overshadows Vietnam's.

Hand digging a new ruby find in the foothills below Mehenge (right), independent Tanzanian miners bag their dirt and gravel before trudging downhill to a nearby stream to screen for gems. Early production suggests a medium-quality mine.

the palace in December 1886. However, chivalry or naiveté cost England a king's ransom. No one thought to search the parade of female servants who shuttled in and out of the palace throughout the night, spiriting away the treasure under their *longyis*.

Today's Mogok is a vastly different place from how gem dealers remember it before 1962. No longer a sleepy rural village, Mogok bustles with more than 100,000 people, a building boom that even includes new hotels, too many trucks, and unusually visible prosperity. New Japanese motorbikes and automobiles crowd the still dusty streets. Government officials estimate that 90 percent of the people earn their living from the gem trade. For years moonlight mining and massive smuggling made this an illicit but powerful economy. Everyone—miners, smugglers, managers, Thai dealers, and buyers—agreed that many more gems left the country illegally than ended up with the government. After all, gem smuggling is commonly known as the world's second oldest profession.

To stem the hemorrhage of ruby smuggling, the Burma government implemented a novel plan to allow private mining partnerships. Citizens obtained two-year leases with the government claiming first choice of everything found. Not satisfied, the military regime next moved in to become everyone's unwelcome partner, skimming a large percentage of each mine's income. This has had two conflicting effects—it is now legal to own and sell gems (which limits smuggling somewhat), but no one wants to pay the military up to 60 percent of his profits (which encourages smuggling).

Fetching prices sometimes exceeding Burma rubies, sapphires from

Umba Valley mine

Kashmir, in what is now northern Pakistan, are favorites among connoisseurs. Unfortunately, the high frozen controversial area, mined for only a few years more than half a century ago, yields little today.

Thailand, whose frenetic expansion recently transformed into the world's largest gem-marketing center, was for several years an important mining source for both rubies and sapphires. In 1990 near Kanchanaburi, three hours west of Bangkok, the 1600-acre S.A.P. facility was the world's largest single sapphire mine. Inside the fence hundreds of miners worked around the clock to wash 8,000 tons of gravel daily, yielding more than 100,000 car-

Sapphires in a profusion of colors are a hallmark of Tanzania's amazing Umba mine (above). Although Australia's sapphire fame rested mainly in inexpensive, dark blue stones, it does produce a large variety of other colors (below).

Outside the main mine at Umba, Tanzania, natives try their luck daily in the Umba River (right). Usually a few minutes of searching through the stream's gravel produces a dozen or more garnets and sapphires.

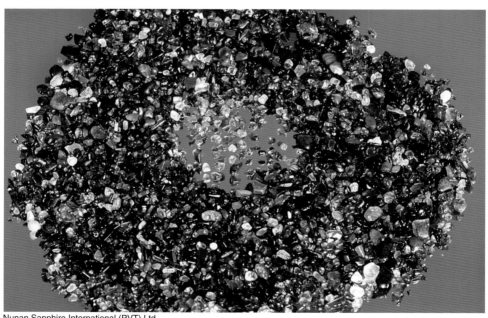
Nunan Sapphire International (PVT) Ltd.

ats of sapphires a week. Proving the wisdom of Sri Lanka's ban on mechanized mining, relentless strip mining reduced this Thai area to a barren moonscape gravel pit in less than a decade.

Thailand's ruby mines used to lie southeast of Bangkok, near the Cambodian border. For years ruby deposits were heavily mined around Chanthaburi, Trat, and Borai. Now ruby mining in Thailand is unproductive. To stay in business, Thai cutting factories depend on rubies from Cambodia, Vietnam, Burma, Madagascar, Tanzania, Kenya, and elsewhere. In Chanthaburi powerful Thai gem families controlled the corundum markets in much of the world and employed tens of thousands of workers. The bubble burst in 1996-1997, when financial markets reacted to the unwarranted expansion into gems and real estate without underlying value. Thailand's economy stumbled and has been slow to recover.

Africa continues to be the best new source for rubies and sapphires. Gems occur across the continent with serious mining in Tanzania, Madagascar, Malawi, and Kenya. Madagascar is producing quality rubies and sapphires as is Malawi. Recently the Tunduru area in Tanzania has been mining good fancy colors that bring good prices.

"Penny Lane" is what local wags call Kenya's string of ruby mines running mainly east to west near the Tanzanian border. Given the volume and quality of their output, they might have been successful had they not fallen prey to the usual greed and corruption that has crippled other African governments. Unusually promising, rubies from Kenya's John Saul Mine compared favorably with Burma's, but few are mined there today.

Cornucopia of color, the fabulous Umba Valley gem deposit glistens with world-class colored gemstones, which Tanzania has had difficulty controlling. Once the most prolific producer of the world's fanciest colored sapphires, today's lease-holders say the mine produces little. What I observed suggests that sapphires still abound. Every time I stopped my vehicle along the unpaved track through the bush, natives appeared with handfuls of multicolored sapphires, garnets, zircons, and chrome tourmalines. One of the most amazing sapphires I own, a two-and-a-half-carat deep raspberry beauty, I bought in a parcel along the road at Umba for five dollars.

Dark blue to opaque midnight blue Australian sapphires used to be the world's largest sellers. From the 1960s to the late 1980s, Aussie miners flooded the market with inexpensive sapphires that wholesaled for $8 to $80 a carat. Simultaneously, while buying almost all of Australia's output, Thai dealers and miners busily tied up production from several African countries and China. Then the Thais hit midnight blue pay dirt at Kanchanaburi. With a plentiful supply of dark sapphires from several sources, Thailand no longer needed Australia.

Unfortunate consequences followed. First, the buying public came to consider sapphires a cheap gem. Retailers filled display cases with inky bluish black sapphires that looked like onyx and told customers the darker the better. For years the residual impact of that episode was that some sellers still find it difficult to persuade buyers that beautiful, transparent blue and multicolored sapphires are gems of value.

My personal gauge for choosing sapphires is this: If a blue sapphire appears black in room light at night, where you wear most gems, then I reject it. In better jewelry there is no excuse for buying opaque or dark sapphires, unless you are collecting black star sapphires, which are beautiful. Why not treat yourself to a brilliant blue, fuchsia, yellow, lavender, teal, or hot pink sapphire? Australian stones (and the darker material from Africa, Thailand, and China) do solve one of the most nagging problems of jewelry making with colored gems. It is expensive and time consuming to match color, cut, and size for pairs and sets. But matching bracelets, earrings, and necklaces are no problem with overly dark sapphires. The future for Australia's dark sapphires may be changing their colors with lattice diffusion (page 35).

Although Montana is a large producer of fine sapphires, it is often overshadowed by overseas sources. Colorful pink sapphires from Rock Creek (right) are the equal of any others in the world. The 1880s find at Yogo Gulch started the first U.S. sapphire rush. Yogo still produces beautiful cornflower blue gems such as the 2.75-carat prize below. Vortex (opposite), the only U.S. underground sapphire mine, one of two firms at Yogo, is currently digging in tunnels 265 feet down.

Roncor, Inc.

Sapphire Gallery, Philipsburg, MT

Montana, one of the world's best-kept mining secrets, astounded me. After a global search for sapphire sources and too many "me-too" blues, the rich color diversity, bicolors, color-change, and uniquely hued sapphires right in our own backyard came as a total surprise. The U.S. has a treasure chest that buyers are just beginning to discover.

The 1880s gold rushers stumbled on sapphires. After tossing out the annoying hard heavy pebbles that clogged their sluices, finally someone recognized the "riffle clutter" as gemstones and sent a package of them to America's first gemologist, Frederick Kunz. He identified the sapphires and sent a check for a handsome amount, asking for more. Tiffany's displayed the gems, and Montana was in the sapphire business.

The best-known deposit is at Yogo Gulch, near the center of the state. Although Yogo sapphires are typically small and flat, their unheated color, dubbed "cornflower blue," is superb. That name, which is often misused when applied to other sapphires, is a rich, lighter blue that holds its hue at night. Yogo's owners justify high wholesale prices (two to three times other Montana sapphires) because of the mine's reputation for quality and its relatively low output. Unlike most other sapphires from Montana or elsewhere, its finely colored gems do not require heating.

Most of Montana's volume comes from the state's southwest, around Gem Mountain and Dry Cottonwood, west of Philipsburg. Brighter, more colorful sapphires including deep to intense blues still lure prospectors and corporate scam artists who continue to plague the state. A robust local cottage industry of cutters and setters is making Americans aware of Montana's mines and of our domestic source of world class gems.

ROMANCING
THE STONE

Most gem crystals look nothing like polished gems. Perfect crystals in their original state, such as diamonds and spinels, occasionally arrive attractive enough to meet our human criteria for beauty, but rarely do specimens look finished enough to collect on their own merits. We want to enhance them. We cut them. We shape them. We facet them. We polish them. Truth be told, we romance them.

Gem crystals are among the hardest and most durable objects on earth. It may come as a surprise that the delicate-appearing jewels gracing slim fingers are usually harder than stainless steel or the front bumper of their owners' fine motorcars. At 9 on the Mohs scale of 1 to 10, rubies and sapphires rank second to diamonds as the world's hardest natural materials. Hardness is a tremendous benefit when you consider purchasing a gemstone.

To attain gem status, a crystal or other material needs two additional characteristics besides durability—beauty and rarity. Rubies and sapphires score high on all three counts. Durability is measurable but beauty and rarity are relative and subject to individual taste. Still, most people can agree that bright clean strong colors are beautiful.

Thousands of years ago, when primitive tribes found crystals, they wore the stones as they came from the ground or water. Because their treasures were harder than any other object in their cultures, early people revered them, believing they possessed magic powers. However, tribesmen lacked today's lapidary techniques to cut, grind, and polish such hard crystals. The concept of putting tiny flat surfaces, or facets, on the gems to catch and reflect light might have occurred to them, but not until Renaissance Europe did jewelers seriously alter or reshape diamonds, rubies, and sapphires.

Ancient jewelry shows that craftsmen attempted to fashion stones into more convenient or attractive shapes. They usually ground gems into crude ovals, circles, squares, and rectangles without much control

Glittering bright as a galaxy, Sri Lanka rubies and sapphires reflect light from tiny internal rutile needles to display classic six-sided stars.
Crab pin from Mayfield's Inc.

Heat treatments vary widely around the world. Little has changed with heating procedures still practiced in rural Sri Lanka (left). By puffing a blowpipe twice a second, a worker can raise the temperature of a 12-carat ruby inside coconut husk charcoal to above 1400° C.

Newer Sri Lankan facilities (bottom, opposite page) use bottled gas for fuel.

In Thailand (below) treaters for years considered their methods a national secret, though they sometimes heated in open, outdoor fires. Now they and U.S. treaters use electric furnaces with sophisticated controls while continually researching to increase their percentages of colorful transparent gems.

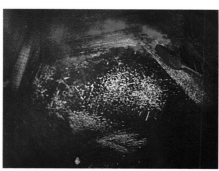

Birthplace of stars...
deep within a Burma ruby (above) shimmer thousands of microscopic rutile needles, here magnified 50 times. Perfectly mimicking the ruby's hexagonal habit, the tiny crystals align at 60° angles, reflecting light in a rare, natural display—a star.

Untreated sapphires from Montana's Eldorado Bar deposit (top right) resemble aquarium gravel more than gemstones.

But look what happens when sapphires are taken to high temperatures in controlled atmospheres. After heat treating alters the internal chemistry (center), some stones intensify to brilliant blues and yellows.

Today, heating is used to permanently improve the color (and clarity) of most rubies and sapphires (right). See also pg 34-35 for the newest treatment, lattice diffusion.

A large trained labor force in Thailand (left and above) facets most of the world's rubies and sapphires at unbeatable prices.

In Sri Lanka (below) hundreds of morning street dealers sell gems. The country encourages new cutting factories (right) as a means of keeping more profits at home.

over symmetry. Because ancients did not know the art and mathematics of faceting, they rounded the tops of crystals into cabochons to reveal more color. Artisans used sand to polish anything with a Mohs hardness up to 7, which includes most gemstones except topaz, spinel, rubies, sapphires, and diamonds. Once the Roman Empire provided trade routes to Asia, caravans returned to Europe with granulated corundum, emery. Emery made it possible to cut and polish all gems except diamonds.

East Indian craftsmen made some of the first efforts to enhance light effects in gems. They even chose the hardest of all gems, diamonds, for their work. Using other diamonds and diamond powder as cutting tools, Indian lapidaries as early as 200 to 400 B.C. put large, flat tables on some of the huge crystals unearthed around Golconda. Even then buyers desired beauty.

Color is the most important feature of rubies and sapphires, but seldom are crystals sold with the same colors that came from the ground. Luck, art, and science combine to achieve marketable hues. Heating, used on various gems at least as early as 2000 B.C. and still the most prevalent of all gem enhancements, improves the color and clarity of the majority of today's rubies and sapphires. At its most elemental, heating is simply men puffing through blowpipes (page 28) to raise the temperature of a coconut charcoal fire to a white-orange glow. Heating has become high-tech art in the laboratories of U.S. treaters John Emmett, Troy Douthit, and Dale Siegford. With sophisticated computer-controlled electric furnaces, they hold temperatures to 5° tolerances in precisely cycled heating-cooling sequences, techniques Thai

31

Whether rubies are found in southern Kenya (above) or along the Thai-Cambodian border (right), most will be cut and polished somewhere in Thailand and marketed in Bangkok. This young Thai woman does "bush cutting" at home in Chanthaburi. Holding dopsticks tipped with inexpensive quarter-carat rubies, she rounds cabochons to be used in earrings and other popular jewelry. Traditionally such stones were heat treated only. Today they might be lattice diffused too.

heaters have quickly copied. Heat treating is inexpensive and permanent.

W e finish what nature forgot," that's the heat treater's motto. To produce royal blue, sapphire crystals must have titanium and iron with proper valence states in adjacent lattice sites. Heaters maximize a stone's color potential by realigning elements and altering valence states. To accomplish the two heating goals—rich color and clarity—heaters raise temperatures to 1750°C or more and control the gaseous atmosphere around the glowing crystals.

Strangely, customers may benefit from buying heat-treated stones. Without heating, rich blue sapphires and the few natural rubies with clean interiors would cost many times more. It is rare to find quality faceted unheated corundum. Because the majority of rough rubies and sapphires are heated soon after they are found, dealers assume, unless there is substantial proof to the contrary, that all rubies and sapphires they sell have been heated. Most customers who even know to ask accept heating as a reality.

Stars, a soft appearance, and collector preference are three valid reasons to keep stones natural. Microscopic rutile needles inside rubies and sapphires create a number of effects that overjoy and frustrate owners and heat treaters. When these crystals-within-crystals line up perfectly at 60°

angles, they can reflect light as a six-pointed star. A small amount of rutile elegantly softens some rare deep blue sapphires from Kashmir, interplaying a subtle light just beneath the surface. Too many needles cloud corundum, making stones "sleepy." Although heating will not remove inclusions, it can dissolve rutile needles. Obviously, no one wants to remove a star or ruin a Kashmir sapphire, so owners leave stars alone and heat only to brighten cloudy stones. After heating, cutters round any remaining cloudy stones into cabochons and facet the rest into bright, eye-catching gems.

Corundum cutting has changed slowly over the centuries. Gem faceting remains traditionbound. The business is mainly Asian because of favorable government policies, experience, and low labor costs. Cabbing operations I saw in northern Burma are right out of the 1500s. Thailand, India, and Sri Lanka cut most of the world's rubies and sapphires. Sri Lankans and Thais have added electric motors in their factories, but some Indian children still spin laps with their feet or use hand-power bow strings.

Cutters occasionally saw or cleave, but despite use of the word "cutting," mostly they shape, facet, and polish crystals by grinding them away with diamond grit. A major change in the 1990s was to standardize (or calibrate) and even automate some gem cutting. Israeli companies market robotic computer-controlled machines to select the best shape for each piece of rough, to preform gems, and to cut and polish diamonds and emeralds. Manufacturers are demanding uniform gem sizes so they can mass-produce precast jewelry. More and more cutting centers are being forced to deliver gems measuring exact millimeter sizes, precision never before required in colored stones.

Market demands challenge tradition in a classic conflict between human and machine, manufacturers and cutters, First and Third World. It is almost impossible for anyone else to compete with Asian prices. Sri Lanka cuts many of its own larger gems, Burma does primitive cutting of gems destined to leave the country both legally and illegally. Hong Kong, Korea, and mainland China are all increasing their abilities in the trade, and India continues to employ a huge labor force to cut a great many small, inexpensive rubies. In Bangkok, Sri Lanka, and Hong Kong, the price can drop to under a dollar a stone for soft material and synthetics, $1 to $2 for uncalibrated gems, and $2 to $5 for calibrated stones. In the U.S. and in Europe, cutters usually charge $15 to $50 a gem for faceting small stones.

Workers hand-cut almost all rubies and sapphires. Because gems sell by weight, trade practice has been to maximize weight and let sizes fall where they may, producing what the trade calls "native cuts," a euphemism for asymmetry. But to compete globally, price-conscious jewelry makers must place precisely-sized gems into precast settings. Thus the dilemma—how to maintain low Asian labor costs, and, at the same time, cut gems to within a 10th of a millimeter?

Lattice Diffusion –
The Newest Gem Treatment

For decades rubies and sapphires have been heated to enhance and intensify their colors. They have usually been sold without disclosure. In 2001 a sudden increase in the number of brightly colored gems and a profusion of sapphires with the much desired pinkish orange "Padparadscha" color sent shockwaves through the trade. Someone had to be creating these new colors, but no one confessed. The world's various gem labs began examining stones. It turns out that Thais developed the new process, which works by diffusing beryllium into gemstones using high heat for hours or days. Now that the process and chemistry are known, labs can detect stones that are not diffused throughout by simple immersion. To detect complete diffusion in valuable gems requires a sophisticated test at a cost of several hundred dollars a stone.

These before-and-after pairs show how various corundum samples from around the world react to the new lattice diffusion treatment.

Most of the above faceted sapphires are from Eldorado Bar and Gem Mountain in Montana. On the left they are seen after standard heat treating and faceting. These stones were salable in this condition but not highly desirable. On the right are the same sapphires after Dr. John Emmett lattice diffused them with beryllium for 33 hours. Note that most stones turned pinkish orange no matter their original color. Two broke apart. Due to the intense heat used, all had to be repolished to remove debris and uneven surfaces.

Lattice diffusion with beryllium produces dramatic changes in corundum from many sources. To the left are almost colorless heated Sri Lanka "geuda" sapphires. Heating turns about half to salable blues. With beryllium the rest become canary yellow. Lattice diffusion transforms Madagascar sapphires (right) from bluish purple to salable rainbow hues.

Sapphires from Montana's Eldorado Bar mine often are dull and colorless, even after heating. Lattice diffusion with beryllium can turn such stones bright orange.

Australia's Rubyvale deposit has a reputation for dark sapphires. With lattice diffusion some remain dark, but a number of the stones turn yellow. orange, and green.

Tanzania's Mehenge mining area is known for rubies. But too many stones from there are not naturally red. With lattice diffusion the area's output can be sold as ruby.

The sudden influx of beautifully-colored pinkish orange sapphires in mid-2001 flooded Thai markets. Prices soared, with buyers and sellers in a frenzy not to miss the action. Over the next year a gem lab in Japan is believed to have issued more than 30,000 reports labeling the new sapphires as Padparadscha. Dealers bought tens of millions of dollars of the attractive mysterious gems.

In the U.S. suspicions rose. By autumn 2001 word was out in the trade that there was something strange about the colors and number of orange sapphires. In January 2002 the AGTA Gemological Testing Center issued an alert to traders. At the February gem shows in Tucson GIA reported beryllium in the colored layers. During the Gem Industry Lab Committee meeting everyone was seeking answers for the trade and gem buyers.

John Emmett, a Ph.D. physicist, gem heat-treater, and sapphire researcher, along with partner Troy Douthit, volunteered to analyze the new orange stones. After more than a year of exhaustive test runs to determine what was altering the gems' colors and chemistry, they completed the comparison pairs you see on these two pages. These stones were coated with a beryllium paste and heated at 1800C. for 33 hours. The small crystals are diffused throughout while the larger pieces are most likely colored no more than half way, still enough to produce new color.

John quickly confirmed that beryllium was responsible for the dramatic color changes. What was surprising was that the same beryllium diffusion treatment that turned some Montana sapphires pinkish orange turned heated almost-colorless Sri Lanka "geuda" sapphires bright yellow. Some unattractively dark Australian sapphires also became orange or yellow. And purple Madagascar crystals transformed to pink, blue, orange, and green.

Thus far, the market for this material and the prices have not stabilized. There are tons of colorless and off-color transparent sapphire in the world. Treating and transforming sapphires into desirable colors challenges the concept of rarity. So too do the prices people are willing to pay for bright gem sapphires. Many in the trade fear that having this much treated material in the market will seriously erode buyer confidence in sapphires.

JEWELS AND ARTIFACTS

T ry imagining history without jewels. Impossible? Yes, these beautiful and fascinating baubles have lit our march through time. There must be reasons why we love them so, reasons buyers rarely consider when they step up to the counter to purchase an engagement ring, a birthday bracelet, or an anniversary necklace. These gorgeous crystals are more than a manifestation of our affection. They are a perfect piece of time preserved.

Jewels played different roles in other centuries. Just one startling realization helps explain the current state of the gem market as well as gem prices. I call it the "democratization of jewelry." In fact, it parallels the democratization of half the world. Before the 1800s gems and jewelry were the playthings of royalty. They also symbolized the "state" and formed part of the state's treasury. Today almost anyone can buy several pieces of jewelry a year. But ponder the prospects of a barmaid or farmer's wife in Elizabethan England receiving a sapphire engagement ring. Preposterous!

So, what has happened? How did we move from a time when kings wore the jewelry and fought for more to a culture that gives 14-year-olds gemstone earrings? Democracy and the Industrial Revolution did it. As soon as wealth was distributed instead of being centered in the castle, workers earned wages instead of meals and began aspiring to own upscale possessions previously reserved for royalty. Gems were high on their wish list. In the 20th century, for the first time in history, anyone with a little money could buy a genuine jewel. Jewelers structured their businesses to service this democratization, to advertise, price, and market to society in general.

While researching, writing, and photographing the gem series for *National Geographic* Magazine for 14 years, I enjoyed an unprecedented opportunity to view firsthand almost all the world's great jewel collections. In addition to the wealth and power the gems represent, one other aspect

The 98.57-carat **Bismarck Sapphire,** *donated in 1967 by Countess Mona von Bismarck, is one of the treasures in Smithsonian's recently renovated Janet Annenberg Hooker Hall of Geology, Gems, and Minerals.*

National Museum of Natural History (Smithsonian Institution), by Chip Clark
Scallop pin from Mayfield's Inc.

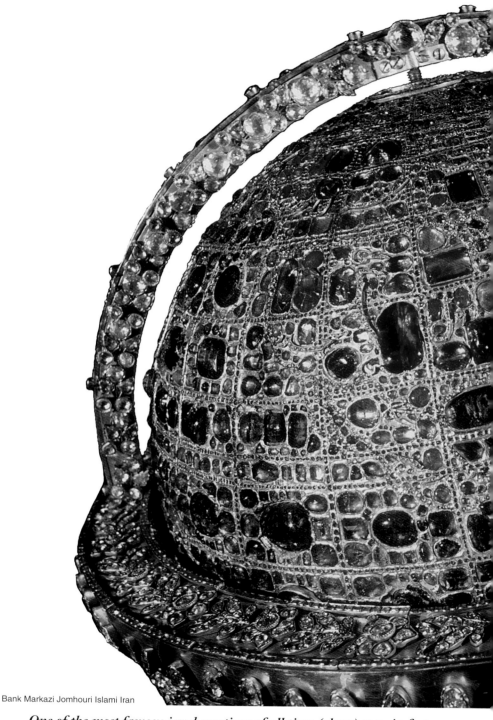

One of the most famous jewel creations of all time (above) was, in fact, a form of inventory control. Fearing theft, an early Persian ruler ordered thousands of his loose gems set into a permanent geographic fantasy.

Standing about a meter high and part of the famous Crown Jewels of Iran, this unique globe has ruby continents, emerald oceans, and diamond accents. The Tehran bank vault has thousands of other gems on display.

impressed me. All the great old treasuries (the Crown Jewels of Iran, the Topkapi gems, the British Crown Jewels) started as loose stone collections. Then, for state occasions master goldsmiths fashioned jewelry, decorative pieces, and crown regalia. In some cases a single gem was reused dozens of ways over the centuries. After all, gems do not age, only their owners do. Various British monarchs have transferred some of their impressive South African diamonds from crown to crown.

One of the most famous gems in the Tower of London has an illustrious history. The *Black Prince Ruby*, not a ruby at all, is a spectacular two-inch long 170-carat spinel. It first appeared in Spain in the 1300s; later, in 1336 the Black Prince in Bordeaux received it for services rendered. Then, in 1367 the jewel surfaced in England on the person of the Prince of Wales. The gem's next appearance was its most noteworthy. In 1415 Henry V donned it as decoration on his battle helmet. Henry was victorious at Agincourt, an event frozen in time by the king's speech as written in Shakespeare's play. The "ruby's" history did not end there. King James admired it so much he had it set in the State Crown, after which it joined the *Cullinan Diamond* as part of the Imperial State Crown.

Another spinel confused with a ruby illustrates the difficulty in identifying and safeguarding gems. London's Victoria & Albert Museum once displayed a collection on loan from the descendants of Plato Zoubov, who had the dubious distinction of being "Catherine the Great's last lover." Among his rewards was a great jewel, which came to be known as the *Zoubov Ruby*. Using information from the family, the V & A's label said it was a spinel, not an uncommon confusion in the 1700s. But on closer examination I

Bracelet courtesy of Sapphire Gallery, Philipsburg, MT   Natural History Museum of Los Angeles County (right)

Some new gem creations are destined to become collection pieces. Years of patience, 49 pink Ceylon sapphires, and a masterly color, size, and shape match combine in this stunning contemporary bracelet. The Hixon Collection in Los Angeles (right) illustrates sapphire's great color variety.

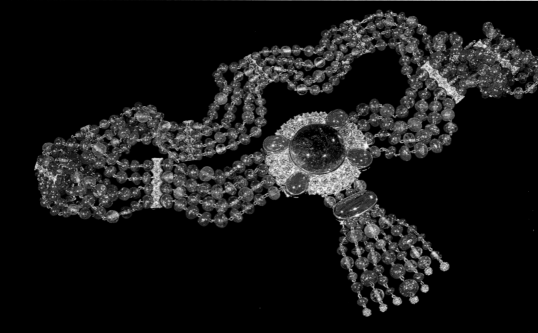

identified it as a flame-fusion synthetic ruby manufactured in this century. Zoubov no doubt received a natural spinel, which somebody probably exchanged in the last few decades. Such switching suggests that historical jewels should be identified and properly labeled before placed on exhibit.

Rubies and sapphires dominate the colored stone trade. Of 30 to 40 popular colored gems these two alone usually account for more than half the world's total sales. But their importance pales in comparison to diamonds. No company has promoted any colored stone worldwide the way De Beers has publicized diamonds. The cartel controls about 55 percent of world rough diamond sales and spends more than $90 million dollars annually promoting diamond purchases in the U.S. alone. Its slogan, "Diamonds are forever," is one of the most recognized in all advertising.

In the colored stone trade there has never been an organization like De Beers. The American Gem Trade Association (AGTA) and the International Colored Gemstone Association (ICA) began widespread gem promotions several years ago. In 1997 ICA spent more than $400,000 for the first international promotion of a colored gemstone—rubies. No single dealer or company could afford such mass-market advertising and promotion for colored gemstones, and no gem trade organization such as AGTA and ICA can match the consumer-awareness display ads in newspapers and magazines and countless television commercials that De Beers uses so brilliantly for diamonds. Thailand and Sri Lanka occasionally mount small promotions for their own national gem trades, but they do not concentrate on single colored stones or advertise globally.

Government of Myanmar

Burma rubies as fine as any ever found were retained by the government for these extraordinary and priceless rings (above). The color and clarity in the 5.56- and 5.25-carat gems illustrate ideal Burma quality.

New York dealer Ralph Esmerian says that when he designed this million-dollar piece (opposite), he envisioned a woman emerging from the sea wearing only this belt. Gem-quality ruby beads form most of the belt, which also includes a 113-carat cabochon emerald and a number of emerald beads.

Sri Lanka is famous for producing large, clean yellow sapphires (below). These superb untreated gems, 91 and 75 carats, were found in the 1960s.

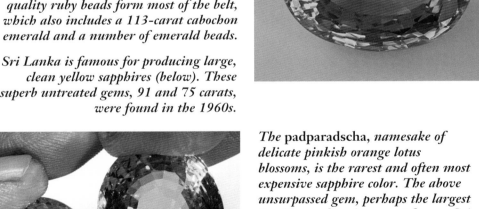

Sri Bhadra Marapana

The padparadscha, *namesake of delicate pinkish orange lotus blossoms, is the rarest and often most expensive sapphire color. The above unsurpassed gem, perhaps the largest "pad" ever found, was cut from a Sri Lanka crystal. Pads are prized by collectors, particularly in Japan, where they bring huge prices.*

True pads are usually said to occur only in Sri Lanka, but dealers often include brownish orange sapphires from Africa in the rare category, advantageously selling them as pads.

43

Gerhard Becker, Idar-Oberstein (2)

Rubies are usually considered the world's most expensive gems. Sold by the carat, which is an ancient weight now standardized as 1/5 gram, or 142 carats to an ounce, some non-gem rubies are so large they are marketed by the kilogram. The Longido mine, in Tanzania, produces huge opaque ruby crystals surrounded by green zoisite, which creates a "watermelon" effect. At the mine (bottom left) workers inspect ruby boulders before exporting. Thai dealers sometimes buy the material, hoping to find edges clear enough to facet.

The bulk of Longido's output ends in Idar-Oberstein, in Germany, where carvers create incredible shapes like the elephant with gold tusks and an American Indian that capitalizes on the two-toned ruby-zoisite interface. One buyer even had a 16-inch-long Mercedes carved for $240,000.

Matching colorless diamonds is easy compared to matching colored gemstones. Hue, brightness, and shape variations among rubies and sapphires increase the combinations toward infinity. Time spent accumulating matched sets costs money. My friend Véronique Ma'Arop matched such gems for Van Cleef & Arpels on Fifth Avenue for years. She says her single most difficult task was assembling rubies or sapphires for a major million dollar necklace, the firm's specialty. "I knew before I started," she laments, "that I had a one- to two-year task before me. I could match sizes. Or I could locate similar shapes. But to get a size, shape, and color match is almost impossible."

Such difficulty in matching blue sapphires explains Australia's success over the past two decades. Its sapphires were so near black that they were easily matched. Sapphires from one huge Thai mining area were popular for the same reason. Often too inky to be truly blue, Kanchanaburi sapphires readily color matched into jewelry. Because gems are most often worn in low-level incandescent lights at night, such inky blue-black stones look more like onyx than sapphires. Fortunately, such sapphires are no longer in favor.

Sapphires are one of the of the gem world's bargains. Their relatively abundance affects price. Compared to diamonds and rubies, little history is associated with them, which results in a lack of recognition. (Chances are the only named sapphires you can think of are stars—the *Star of India, Star of Lanka, Star of Asia, Star of Bombay, Midnight Star.* The famous named diamonds, the *Hope, Cullinan, Koh-i-noor, Eugenie, Tiffany,* are synonymous with history as well as beauty.) And the easy availability of inexpensive sapphires over the past two decades led a generation of buyers to believe that sapphires are dull and dark, thus forgetting that fine, richly-colored sapphires are as rare and valuable as other gems—but priced lower.

Good rubies are so rare that few jewelers or buyers ever see them. No matter the source, a ruby, to be really valuable, has to be really red. Purple, pink, and fuchsia are not red. And despite what you will hear repeatedly, there is no such color as "pigeon blood." In fact, I know a frustrated ruby mine owner in Africa who flew to Burma, bought eleven pigeons, and took them and a Buddhist priest down to the ocean at midday. With chanting in the background, he chopped off each bird's head, dripped the blood onto his fingers, and waited the prescribed two minutes before looking. According to the samurai miner, instead of the desired prime Burma color, it was all "hot pink." Not one pigeon bled deep ruby red.

Fellow gem writer Richard Hughes, who studied corundum from his former Bangkok home-base, and I agree that a major contributor to the allure of Burma ruby color is fluorescence. As we will learn in the next chapter, trace amounts of chromium (sometimes less than one percent) are responsible for the red color in rubies. This impurity also causes rubies to fluoresce under ultraviolet light or even in sunlight, giving Burmese rubies, which contain more chromium than most others, their appealing red glow. Some Thai rubies may actually be redder than Burma rubies, but they lack the same fluorescence. Prized though it may be, Burma's red is no longer unique. Rubies from the relatively recent Vietnam mines look remarkably similar. In

Perfection in jewelry is the mark of a master. London's Laurence Graff displays the talent that raised him to the top of the gem trade. Designed and faceted in Graff's workshops, the matched heart-shaped and emerald-cut Burmese sapphires took months to assemble. Total gem weight in the magnificent necklace: 185 carats. Each of the perfectly matched earring sapphires is 38 carats. Notice that each piece is set with the minimum of metal in order to maximize the intrinsic beauty of the sapphires themselves.

A Burma sapphire worth a royal ransom was used for this 19ᵗʰ-century Buddha carving (right). Now, without royal patrons, artisans seldom have the luxury of time to sculpt quality gems.

The British Museum (Natural History) London

London's Laurence Graff continues to amaze the gem world with evermore beautiful jewelry confections. This time the focus is sapphires matched in size, shape, and color (left). Such matches result from long searches and major recutting to create museum-quality classics.

fact, the first few Vietnam rubies sent to gemological labs around the world for identification were erroneously classified as "Burma rubies." That was not surprising because the crystals are actually from the same geological area.

The world's most exciting recent corundum discoveries include colorful new rubies and sapphires from Madagascar and Malawi, neon-bright "hot pink" sapphires from Vietnam along with rubies from Mong Hsu, Burma, and various sapphire colors from Tunduru and Songea in Tanzania.

Some consumers wonder about their gems fading. "My ring looks great now, but will the color last?" With rubies and sapphires the answer is yes. The color you love will still be bright and lively fifty million years from now. Whereas it is true that some kunzite, topaz, morganite, and amethyst may fade over time and exposure to light, the colors in most gems are stable. The color results from impurities altering the structure of crystals, so the crystal itself acts as a color filter. With a moderate amount of care your rubies and sapphires will remain colorful and beautiful forever.

Blue sapphire and diamond suite by Graff, London

47

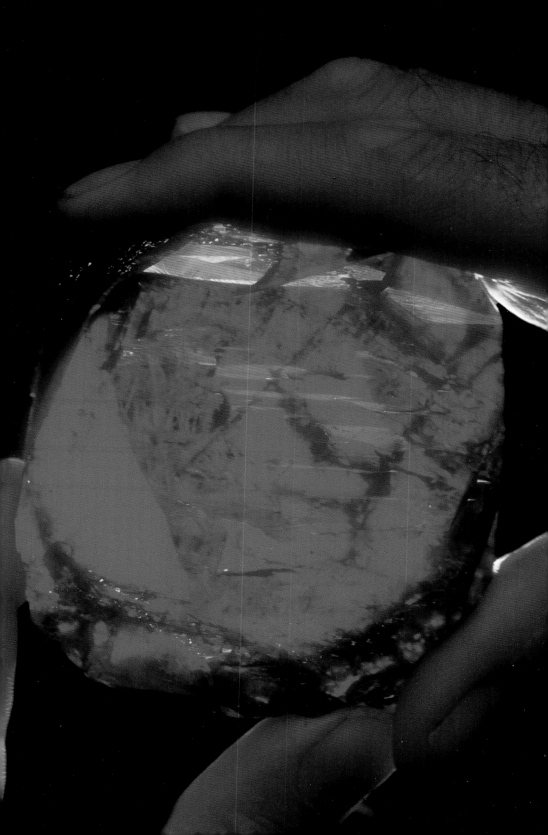

LAB-GROWN CORUNDUM AND SIMULANTS

The man in the front row grew more and more animated during one of my frequent gem talks. I sensed his excitement as he realized his choices between natural and lab-grown rubies and sapphires. I continued projecting a selection of slides illustrating man-made corundum in jewelry, watches, lasers, microchips, and other industrial applications.

"Are you telling me those rubies and sapphires were grown to be exactly the same chemically as naturals?" he questioned.

"Yes, that's right," I assured him.

"And they're flawless for just a few dollars a carat?"

"Right," I repeated. "And you can get them in almost any shape, size, and color."

"Then," he wondered aloud, "why would anyone spend thousands for natural rubies and sapphires when you can get one of those perfect synthetics for a few dollars? Which should I buy?"

"It depends on what you want, " I replied, and here is what else I told him.

There are legitimate reasons for rubies' wide price variations. Understanding pricing will make you a smarter buyer. Six types of rubies are marketed—naturals and at least five different lab-grown varieties, which the trade calls "synthetics," the scientifically correct term that seems to confuse the public. Begin by applying the three traditional criteria for gems—beauty, which in colored stones means great color; rarity; and durability. I propose the gem trade adds a fourth criterion—naturalness. Humans place a premium on nature and things natural. Manufactured materials may be hard and beautiful, but they lack rarity and that special aspect of being formed in the earth. Thus, this natural factor, perceived value, supply, and demand all determine price.

"Natural" means what it says. The trade defines it specifically as a gem formed by nature. In the strictest sense, natural also carries a second,

John Chatham, at Chatham Created Gems, grew this gem-quality 2134-carat ruby crystal using the flux-grown process developed by his father.

H. Djévahirdjian S.A., Monthey, Switzerland

The world's biggest synthetic corundum producer, H. Djévahirdjian S.A., in Monthey, Switzerland (above), makes flame-fusion rubies and sapphires by the ton in a process largely unchanged since 1902. Two thousand furnaces burn around the clock to grow corundum for watch crystals, bearings, and inexpensive jewelry.

Century Time calls its unique all-sapphire waterproof timepiece "the watch that is a jewel" (below left). This latest scam (below) comes from Cambodia, where a boule of man-made flame-fusion ruby worth only a few dollars was broken into chunks and chemically etched to look natural. Sellers risk their lives by asking a fortune for such faked pieces.

Century Time, Biel, Switzerland

Terry Coldham (52 carat piece of flame-fusion boule)

Flame-fusion crystals form fast. A single crystal boule of synthetic corundum (above) grows in 5 to 16 hours. The process is deceptively simple. Fine aluminum oxide powder with metallic oxides for color melts as it falls through flames and drops onto pedestals, where it crystallizes into a boule. Depending on additives, any color is possible.

Tiny doughnuts of red corundum (below) reduce friction and wear in Swiss watches. Synthetic ruby bearings are harder than spinning steel shafts they hold in place. Machinists once hand-drilled holes. Now, powerful lasers (above) burn precise circles through microscopic discs for compasses, electric meters, and new-age electronic products.

The world's two former synthetic gem ruby crystal growers melted metallic powders to create "flux," a molten simulation of the earth's magma. They added the ingredients of rubies, aluminum oxide and chromium, to crystallize. John Chatham (left) extracts ruby crystals from hardened flux at Chatham Created Gems.

Judith Osmer (right) empties still-glowing molten flux to harvest rubies after a multi-month crystallization cycle. The ruby below grew inside a platinum cup.

Chatham Created Gems

J.O. Crystal Co. (2)

more refined definition at an even higher price: a stone that has not been heated, irradiated, diffused, or enhanced. Rubies, like emeralds, are sometimes oiled or even "glass-filled" to mask inclusions. A precious few gemstones formed by nature have everything—beauty, rarity, and durability—which keeps them in high demand at high prices. Prices for natural rubies soar from more than $2000 a carat for commercial grades, to $25,000 a carat for fine jewels, up to a breathtaking $225,000 a carat for larger specimens.

L ab-grown crystals have the same chemistry and characteristics as natural crystals. Gemology borrowed the word "synthetic" from science, where, by definition, a synthetic material is a human-made duplicate. Five types of corundum synthetics are sold. Flame-fusion rubies and sapphires, the least expensive synthetics at just pennies a carat, enjoy wide use in both jewelry and industry. Flux-grown rubies, sold only as gems, cost several hundred dollars a carat. Czochralski-melt or -pulled rubies and sapphires, are indispensable in high-tech applications. Hydrothermal sapphires are the fourth type. Today's largest single crystals, up to 65 kilograms, are produced by Crystal Systems Inc. using its Heat-Exchanger Method.

"Simulants" are not synthetics but inexpensive look-alikes. Cubic zirconia, when used to imitate diamonds or corundum, are simulants.

Only once did synthetic gems disrupt the market for naturals. Almost as long as people have worn adornments, they have dreamed of creating gems. Until the end of the 19th century, their fantasy had met with about the same success as transforming lead or straw into gold. Then, in 1891-

92 in sealed letters to the Paris Academy of Science, Auguste Verneuil, a modern-day Rumpelstiltskin, described a new crystal-growing process. When Verneuil introduced his rubies in 1902, they caused a sensation. He became the first synthesizer of precious gems, which he said were "equal to nature's finest." Because jewelers and customers had no way of differentiating naturals from synthetics, prices for naturals plummeted. By 1907 production exploded to five million carats of rubies a year. That sudden influx relegated synthetics to low-priced commodities, and it took years for naturals to return to prices that accurately reflected their rarity.

The availability of inexpensive, uniform material led to a Swiss relationship that remains at the heart of synthetic ruby production. The idea for jewel watch bearings to reduce wear and friction began in England in 1704. In 1830 the Swiss opened a natural ruby bearing factory, and by 1850 most Swiss watch movements pivoted on tiny natural ruby doughnuts. Verneuil changed the industry with less expensive, more uniform synthetics. He originally envisioned his material as gems, but industrial applications became a larger market. Today, H. Djévahirdjian S.A. in Monthey, Switzerland grows 80 tons (more than 350 million carats) of lab-grown rubies, sapphires, and spinel annually. About 70 percent of the production goes to watch crystals. Crystals of most watches that sell for $400 or more are slices of colorless lab-grown sapphire. Transparent, strong, and impervious to chemicals and scratching (except by diamonds), sapphire is perfect for the task. At pennies a carat, flame-fusion gems form the low end of the market. They compete directly with colored cubic zirconia, rhinestones, the least

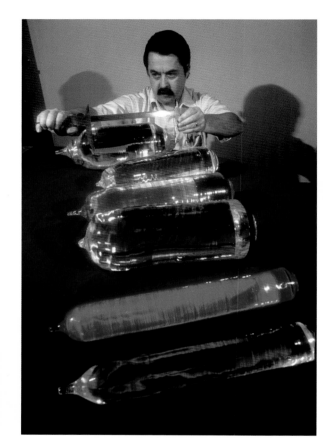

Huge synthetic sapphire and ruby boules (left) pass stringent final inspection at Saint-Gobain Crystals and Detectors.

Engineers specify sapphire substrates, which naturally resist errant radiation, for microchips in satellites and military gear (above). More than 500,000 Saphikon sapphire windows on laser checkout counters resist scratches for years (right).

expensive colored crystals from overseas, and glass or plastic imitations.

A big step up in price and rarity occurred with lab-grown rubies and sapphires made by an entirely different method. Two U.S. firms, one operated by the Chatham brothers, in San Francisco, and the other by Judith Osmer, in Los Angeles, used to make most of the world's flux-grown rubies. The Chathams' father, Carroll, grew the world's first flux-grown gems—emeralds—in the 1930s, and John Chatham's research led to successful ruby production in 1978.

Gems grown in flux are a costly, time-consuming venture. As the first outsider ever to see inside the Chatham facility, I can verify that flux-grown gems are an expensive and dangerous business. First John Chatham melted metallic powders in pure platinum crucibles at temperatures up to 1200° C. The flux mixture became the host where gems formed. Into the brew he added small ruby seed crystals and the constituents of rubies, aluminum oxide and chromium. If everything worked right, in 9 to 12 months he would cool the furnaces and hammer apart the hardened flux ball. The new ruby crystals are seen falling onto a table (page 52).

Of all the synthetics, flux-grown gems look the most like naturals. They even have inclusions, which Tom Chatham says "seem to be part of the growth process. If we knew how to make our gems flawless, we would. We

Sapphire window from Saphikon - Saint-Gobain, Milford, NH

lose a lot of material in manufacturing and more in cutting because of inclusions. Our crystals are subject to the same stresses and growth processes as naturals." True, except there is no geopressure or movement. Unfortunately, neither Chatham nor Osmer grows crystals now. Judy retired and Tom buys product created to his specs by overseas crystal growers.

S ynthetic crystals grown by several different processes are more at home in research labs than jewelry boxes. Invaluable to industry, rubies and sapphires are stretching the limits of technology. When creating the first laser, Union Carbide (now part of Saint-Gobain Crystals and Detectors) considered a wide variety of materials. Chromium, the element that makes rubies red, also causes them to fluoresce, which is the vital feature that makes a laser work. A flawless chromium-doped synthetic ruby rod was the heart of the world's original laser. Lab-grown sapphires fill many high-tech roles.

Synthetic sapphires provide a solution necessary for communications satellites and nuclear defense systems. Radiation either from the sun or atomic blasts can cause errors in microchips. When stray charged particles penetrate circuits, they travel through traditional silicon substrates, upsetting normal readings. Sapphire, an almost perfect insulator, naturally "radiation hardens" circuits. Over the past few years manufacturers replaced traditional

One Man Dreamed of Turning Cultured Laser Crystals Into Huge Corundum Gems

Flawless natural rubies and sapphires 100 carats or more are not available. But cultured or lab-grown corundum boules of thousands of carats are routinely grown for a large variety of high-tech applications. E. Bud Erickson developed lasers from such material. Then he had the idea to facet some of these perfect crystals into gigantic gems.

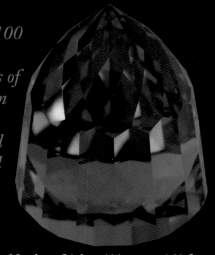

Northern Lights; 411 carats, 161 facets

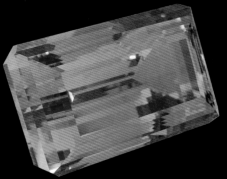

The Dawning; 925 carats, 81 facets

Daughter of My Heart; 180 carats, 177 facets

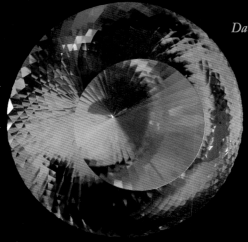

Galaxis; 1784 carats, 961 facets

Stardust; 709 carats, 193 facets

silicon-on-silicon chips with Silicon-on-Sapphire (SOS) in military and communication satellites and in microcircuits for missiles, fighter planes, tanks, and battlefield installations. Saphikon's innovative creation, "pulled" single-crystal sapphire domes, once protected the nosecone sensors of heat-seeking missiles. During months of training flights, airborne sand and other debris abraded traditional crystal missile windows. Now Saphikon makes large flat sapphire windows to cover fighter planes' infrared detection systems. Its esoteric product line also includes tiny sapphire tubes incorporated into automatic blood-sampling machines (because blood won't coagulate on single-crystal sapphire), and surgical tips for medical lasers. Using their Heat Exchanger Method, Crystal Systems grows the world's largest sapphire boules, up to 65 kilos. The newest "Next Great Things" are Blue LEDs that may replace incandescent and fluorescent bulbs. Supported by sapphire substrates, the LEDs can last 10 years on a fraction of today's power. Traffic signals use the LEDs already.

You come into weekly contact with a piece of sapphire larger than a queen's tiara, although it is never identified as such. Supermarket checkout counters need hard, clear windows so lasers can "read" product bar codes. A few days of dragging cans across early glass windows produced scratches that interfered with readings. The top $1/32$ inch of today's laser windows, made by Saphikon, is pure sapphire. Less-hard stainless steel frames may need replacing, but sapphires in use 10 years show no wear.

Simulants are a persistent threat to gem buyers, and today's variety of fakes is staggering. Were these imitations represented and sold at honest prices, they would offer an alternative for inexpensive jewelry. But all too often unscrupulous vendors dupe the unwary. From its pre-Roman origin, glass continues to be the most common imitation gemstone. A whole new chemical stew of competitive materials makes differentiating fakes difficult for the casual buyer.

A prevalent fake difficult to detect is a gem sandwich. The stone's top is often genuine but off-color ruby or sapphire. The bottom may be glass, synthetic ruby or sapphire, or blue or red synthetic spinel. There may be a center slice, making it a triplet. A $10 price would be fine; offered for $1000 a carat, it is robbery. The most common scams today involve selling synthetic gems as naturals or trying to sell inexpensive gems as something else, such as offering aquamarines as sapphires or garnets as rubies. See page 50 for another in the endless series of deceptions.

My best advice continues to be, buy from dealers you know and trust to stand behind their products. Be wary when you shop outside recognized stores. A tourist without gem training is fair game when away from home or in Third World street markets. Carry a magnifier. Look for inclusions. Glass is typically clean inside except for tiny gas bubbles, whereas natural gems usually have characteristic identifying inclusions. Before you purchase an expensive gem, request a report from a recognized gemological laboratory. If you live in the United States, use a U.S. lab. The more you learn about gems, the more successful you will be at getting what you want and what you pay for.

Buying and Caring

Buyers of fine jewelry frequently ask two questions, Where should I shop? and What is the best way to take care of my purchase? The answers to both are important. By choosing wisely, you can avoid disappointment and save money. When I speak to groups or clients, I give them as many facts as possible. I believe that the more you know, the better you can buy. Having information will help you own a gem of lasting beauty; give the perfect gift, especially a ruby for a July birthday or a sapphire for a September birthday; or create a piece of wearable art.

Of course, rubies are red, and sapphires come in every conceivable color. Although blue is certainly the most recognized and most purchased sapphire color, dazzling sapphire jewelry also features yellow, pink, orange, green, gold, teal, and colorless stones. Why not put a rainbow in your life with an array of sapphires?

Customers feel confident when they know what they are buying has inherent value. But there is one illusion I want to dispel immediately. No matter what the signs say, there is no such thing as "wholesale to the public." Stores cannot afford to sell at wholesale to retail customers, unless your brother owns a jewelry store. Everybody has to make a profit. A jewelry store is a business like any other. The owner pays rent or mortgage, taxes, salaries, inventory, advertising, office expenses, and training, plus some extraordinary expenses such as insurance and security. The store will not sell at a loss, so be leery of discounters with continuous sales. Such "sale prices" are their retail.

What you can seek is to pay the least amount for the quality you want. By following a few sensible practices, you can learn to buy smart. With a little research you can gather the information you need. Begin with newspaper ads by regular jewelry stores and discounters, and then window-shop. Allocate a few days to check prices and quality at several retailers. An intense hue raises the cost of a colored gem enormously. Compare apples

A sumptuous array of glittering Montana sapphires lures color-conscious buyers to America's own high-quality gemstone.

Sapphire Gallery, Philipsburg, MT
Dolphin pin by Mayfield's Inc.

Bracelets and ring, Sapphire Gallery, Philipsburg, MT; watch, private collection, Bangkok, Thailand

Mined and designed in the U.S.A., the multihued Montana sapphires in the above bracelets and ring are durable and beautiful. The elegant jewelry watch features matched diamonds and Thai sapphires. To keep a bright new look, wash sapphires in warm water with mild soap or detergent, or have them cleaned ultrasonically.

with apples. An unfair sales technique is to show you a heavily included ruby with mediocre color and insist that it is very clean with great color. By examining many stones, you can learn to recognize important differences.

Having lived about half my life overseas, I know bargaining to be an honorable business practice in many countries. Generally, quality stores in the U.S. do not bargain. A store will inform you if it sells only at marked prices. A considerable benefit from a reputable jewelry store is its high-quality ongoing service. You will have a resource for information, cleaning, repairs, and additional matching pieces. Discounters and mail order firms advertise low prices partly because they provide little or no service. A favorite practice among such retailers is to raise prices five times wholesale, hold a half-price sale, and still net more than most jewelry stores.

You have other buying options. Designers and goldsmiths can work with you to make custom jewelry. Personal shoppers can buy for you. The important consideration is to find gems and settings that appeal to you.

When you purchase an expensive gem, I recommend obtaining a laboratory report verifying color, clarity, size, finish, etc. The Gemological Institute of America, AGTA Gemological Testing Center, EGL-USA, and other reputable U.S. and European labs provide expert service. Ask your jeweler which labs issue reports that the trade respects.

Leave serious decisions involving gemstones to experts. This 10-carat ruby (right) recently sold at auction for one million dollars with a visible chip on its edge. Although an owner might choose to hide the imperfection with a prong, the responsible dealer opted to have the ruby recut, losing part of a gem valued at $100,000 a carat. Recutting is an option for old gems too. Many antique stones lack the brilliance achievable with modern cuts. Sacrificing weight when recutting may increase the value of your heirloom.

Finally, there is the question of value. I wrote earlier of gems as concentrated, portable wealth. Historically, fine gems maintain value better than many other luxuries. Dealer Jack Abraham estimates rubies are 50 times rarer than diamonds but cost only a few times more for similar size and quality. In today's market, rubies appear to be a comparative bargain. A bigger bargain is sapphires, which sell for hundreds to thousands of dollars a carat instead of the tens of thousands a carat that top-quality emeralds, diamonds, and rubies command.

Buy the best ruby or sapphire you can afford. Because a clean gem is usually stronger than a more included one, it can easily withstand daily wear. Some of my clients consider durability, rarity, and uniqueness as important as beauty. Realize that almost all rubies and sapphires are heated to enhance their colors and improve clarity. Assume your gem is heated unless specifically told otherwise. Increasingly common is adding "glass-like" fillers, such as borax to rubies, to mask inclusions and improve a gem's appearance. Whether a by-product of heating or a deliberate treatment in a ruby, such enhancement should be disclosed. Lattice diffusion, once called bulk diffusion, is the most troublesome of the new enhancements. Using high heat, this process diffuses chemicals into the stone. Although it dramatically improves color, unbeknown to dealers and the public, this process has been used for perhaps three years without disclosure. Conse-

Burma ruby ring and sapphires
from Precious Gem Resources

Nature's finest, most perfect creations capture time in wearable form, forever new, eternal. When you buy rubies and sapphires, you own the rainbow.

quently, tens of thousands of diffused rubies and sapphires have already been sold without paperwork or disclosure. Such an unethical practice makes getting a new gem lab report doubly important for any medium- to high-quality ruby or sapphire you buy.

Shopping away from home often brings disappointment. Most often you will do better buying from someone you know and trust. Getting satisfaction may be difficult if you bought your gem overseas. Remember, Thai dealers were selling the diffused gems on pages 34-35 for two years before alert buyers and gemologists suspected trouble. If you bought a diffused orange sapphire for $10,000 and found it was worth only $500, how would you feel? Honest dealing is what you expect and deserve. Normally this is no problem. Most of the time when people get into trouble buying gems, they are looking for a "deal." There are almost never deals with gems. As a result of global communications, gems have a global price, which fluctuates with supply and demand. Dealers around the world pay about the same for similar stones. Loose gemstones enter the U.S. duty free, so there is no monetary benefit to buying overseas.

Learn all you can, shop wisely with a known firm, and get a quality lab report. Then you can enjoy the experience of purchasing a great gem. Whatever your preference—ruby or sapphire—wise gem buying promises excitement and reward. In the end, jewelry is a better more permanent gift than a bouquet of flowers or a box of candy. Visually stimulating and satisfying, rubies and sapphires are everlasting.

Montana sapphires from Fred Ward

62

Large—clean—red—what more could a buyer desire from rubies? If you are shopping for a fine gem, buy a natural stone. The suite on the right looks like great naturals, but every one is lab-grown, worth a fraction the price of naturals. The top three are Czochralski-pull gems, the center ovals are flame fusion, and the remaining five are flux-grown.

Here is why you need all the help you can get when buying fine gems. Consult an expert.

Look at the 10 gems above. Each is a ruby. Would you pay $10,000 for one? Or $1000? How about a dollar? And the 17 sapphires below? Is the best value a blue or a yellow, orange, pink, or purple? The typical gem buyer is at a distinct disadvantage without solid support. There is no way you could make a reasonable decision without doing some serious gemological study—or consulting an expert. Buying a fine gem is not like buying a car or house, where the attributes are obvious. With gem purchases you need honest, trustworthy information from people who will stand behind their merchandise and be there if and when you need help.

Caring for rubies and sapphires is easy because they are almost perfect gems—rare, beautiful, and durable. At Mohs 9 they are harder than all other gems except diamonds. They will scratch anything they contact except diamonds and only diamonds will scratch them, so keep your rubies and sapphires away from softer gems, from each other, and from diamond jewelry. Store your jewelry separately, preferably in soft bags. As your gemstones are harder then gold, platinum, or silver, avoid letting gems touch jewelry mounts.

Almost any cleaning technique works on most rubies and sapphires. You can use ultrasonic cleaners, steamers, warm soapy water, and brushes. Avoid mechanical cleaners for heavily fractured gems or oiled rubies. Steam or ultrasonic cleaning might remove the oil. Simple regular cleaning and care will help keep your gems sparkling for a lifetime.

Phillip Youngman, a fine young faceter, cut all these natural sapphires.

63

Gemstones are sold by weight, not by size or volume. This significant difference makes them more like gold and silver than other luxury products such as furs, yachts, automobiles, or watches. Because gems are composed of different chemical elements, they do not all weigh the same. Therefore, gemologists use weight as one means of identification.

Weight, or density, is expressed as specific gravity (SG). Diamond has an SG of 3.52, which means a diamond weighs 3.52 times as much as the same volume of water. With an SG of 4, quite high for gems, rubies and sapphires are heavier than diamonds. In practical terms they are dense, with a solid, hefty feel. They also vary in size from other gems of the same weight.

Gems are weighed in carats (not to be confused with *karat*, which refers to the purity of gold). A carat, from the ancient Indian use of carob seeds for small consistent weights, equals $1/5$ gram, or $1/142$ ounce. Sizes are measured in millimeters (see below). A round one-carat diamond, a standard in the trade, is typically 6.5mm in diameter. A round one-carat ruby or sapphire, being denser, measures only 6.1mm across. So, rubies and sapphires of the same weight as a similarly cut diamond are physically smaller. It is necessary to factor in size when choosing settings.

Cutting proportions vary far more in colored stones than in diamonds, especially with Third World cutters. When buying, the main considerations after color and clarity are the quality of the cutting and the final proportions. Beauty is a major component in the "make" of a colored gem.

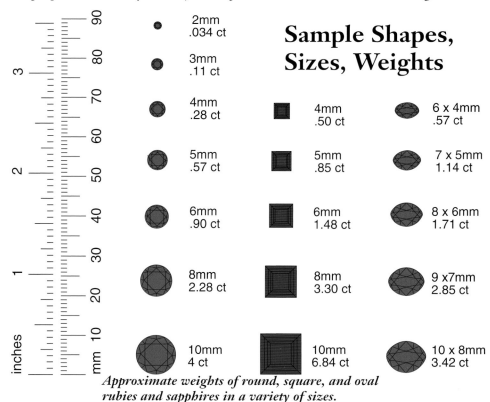

Sample Shapes, Sizes, Weights

2mm .034 ct					
3mm .11 ct					
4mm .28 ct	4mm .50 ct		6 x 4mm .57 ct		
5mm .57 ct	5mm .85 ct		7 x 5mm 1.14 ct		
6mm .90 ct	6mm 1.48 ct		8 x 6mm 1.71 ct		
8mm 2.28 ct	8mm 3.30 ct		9 x7mm 2.85 ct		
10mm 4 ct	10mm 6.84 ct		10 x 8mm 3.42 ct		

Approximate weights of round, square, and oval rubies and sapphires in a variety of sizes.